بســـم الله الرحمن الرحيـــم

Scribe الكاتب

This book belongs to

First published in the United Kingdom in 1431^AH (2010^CE) by Learning Roots Ltd.
Unit 6, TGEC, Town Hall Approach Road, London, N15 4RX.
www.learningroots.com

Reprinted in 1433^AH (2012^CE).

Copyright © Learning Roots 2010

Authorship, graphic design & illustrations by the Learning Roots Education Design Service.

Acknowledgements
The publisher thanks Allah, Lord of the Worlds, for making this publication possible.

British Library Cataloguing in Publication Data
A CIP catalogue record for this book is available from the British Library in London.

Printed and bound in China

ISBN: 978-1-905516-29-2

Scribe™ allows you to achieve beautiful Arabic handwriting with precision guidance, leaving you to practice your skills to perfection. The secret of the Scribe™ approach is simple: it's everything an outstanding handwriting practice resource should have.

Exclusively Tailored Typeface

When Arabic script comes to mind, many visualize its rendition in calligraphic form. Yet despite its beauty and proportioned shape, calligraphy cannot be produced except with specialist writing instruments. The common round-nib pen or pencil is simply unable to reproduce wide-to-narrow strokes that constitute calligraphic letters.

Modern advances by font foundries have produced some stunning new Arabic typefaces, some of which are formed by single-width strokes. Many of these typefaces however, contain accentuated components rendering them unsuitable for the teaching of Arabic handwriting to beginners.

In publishing Scribe™, Learning Roots designed an exclusive typeface that combines the proportioned form of the most renowned style of Arabic calligraphy, Naskh, along with the single-width stroke common to the round-nib pen. The result was **Kitābah**™, a wonderful Arabic typeface perfect for those seeking to establish a firm grounding in Arabic handwriting.

Guidelines

Scribe™ supports consistent letter formation through the use of both horizontal and vertical guidelines, ensuring a proportioned height and width ratio for each letter. Guideline support is gradually reduced as the book progresses until complete removal at the end of the book, thus apportioning support to when it most needed.

Gradual Size Reduction

The size of the typeface is gradually reduced as the book progresses until it reaches a typical handwriting size at the end of the book. Forming large letters in the early stages helps support the accuracy of hand-eye coordination and makes it easier to check the correct visual translation of letter forms and strokes. Once these skills are perfected, a reduction in the typeface size is better facilitated.

Practice to Perfection

Scribe™ provides ample opportunity to practice each letter and word formation, with a proportionally higher number of repetitions in the early stages, thus nurturing the writer's skill and confidence. Opportunities are also afforded to trace over words in the initial stages of introduction to help ensure a guided start on a sure footing.

Comprehensive Foundational Approach

Scribe™ affords much focus to the strengthening of the foundations of a skilled writer. Hence it moves the writer from basic letter formation, to all permutations of joins, to words and then to sentences, gradually introducing advanced instruction as the course progresses.

Focus on Form

Handwriting practice has a specific purpose, and for many it is to perfect the shape and form of their letters and words. Scribe™ realizes this and focuses on what matters, whilst still providing common Arabic words and Hadeeth as practice examples.

Contents

Letters: *Practicing letters in their common stand-alone forms.*
Letters at the Beginning, Middle and End of a Word: *Exploring the variation of letter forms when they appear at the beginning, middle and end of a word.*
Words: *Understanding the application of letter joins learned in the previous sections through words.*
Sentences: *Completing the final stage with progression from sentences to paragraphs.*

الحروف Letters

Letters are the foundation of your words and sentences, so build
a strong foundation by practicing your letters to perfection.
For each letter, begin by tracing over the grey outline and then
produce your own repetitions. Take special care to use the
guidelines to ensure the correct height, width and positioning of
each letter. This chapter begins with a short alphabet test that is
repeated at the end of the chapter to help track your progress.

Quick Start
Begin by writing all the letters in the Arabic alphabet. There are no guidelines here, leaving you to determine your progress when you repeat this exercise at the end of the letters section.

خ	ح	ج	ث	ت	ب	ا
ص	ش	س	ز	ر	ذ	د
ق	ف	غ	ع	ظ	ط	ض
ي	و	ه	ن	م	ل	ك

4

خ	ح	ج	ث	ت	ب	ا
ص	ش	س	ز	ر	ذ	د
ق	ف	غ	ع	ظ	ط	ض
ي	و	ه	ن	م	ل	ك

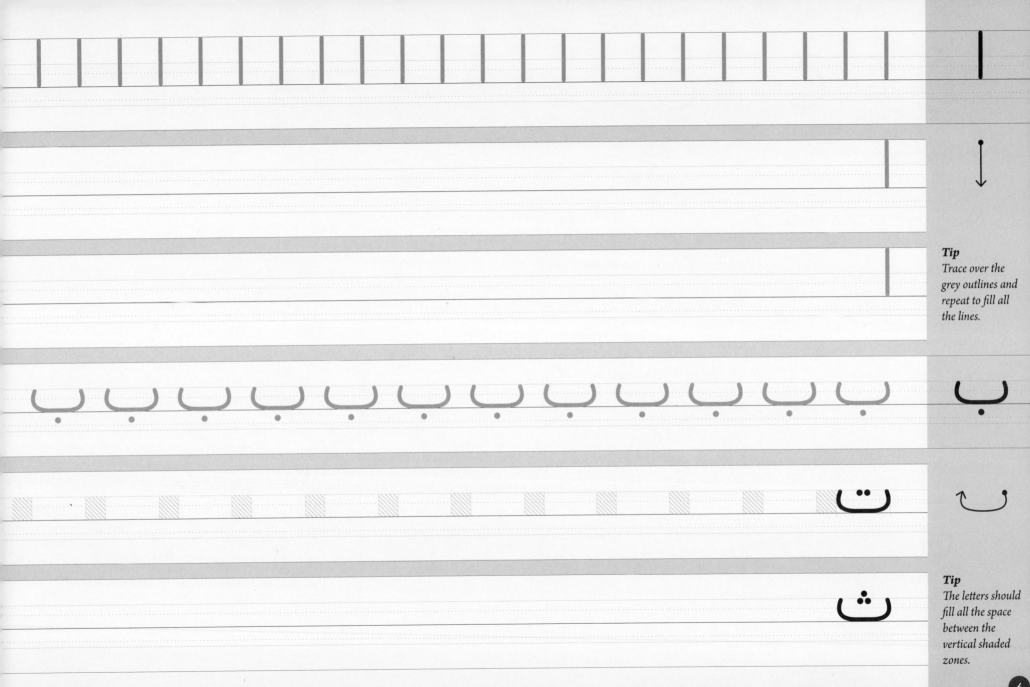

ا

↓

Tip
*Trace over the
grey outlines and
repeat to fill all
the lines.*

بـ

↶

تـ

Tip
*The letters should
fill all the space
between the
vertical shaded
zones.*

ثـ

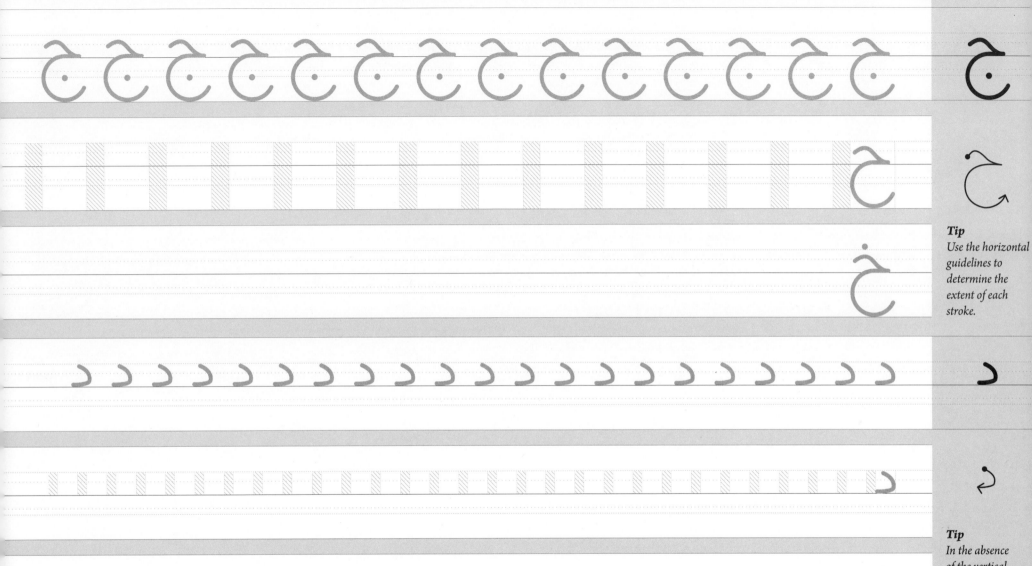

Tip
Use the horizontal guidelines to determine the extent of each stroke.

Tip
In the absence of the vertical shaded zones, keep focused to maintain the correct letter width.

ر ر ر ر ر ر ر ر ر ر ر ر ر ر ر ر ر ر ر

ر

ر

ز

س س س س س س س س س س س س س س

س

س

ش

ص ص ص ص ص ص ص ص ص ص

ص ص

ض

ﻃ ﻃ ﻃ ﻃ ﻃ ﻃ ﻃ ﻃ ﻃ ﻃ ﻃ ﻃ ﻃ ﻃ ﻃ ﻃ

ﻃ

ﻅ

ع ع ع ع ع ع ع ع ع ع ع ع ع ع ع ع

ع

غ

ف ف ف ف ف ف ف ف ف ف ف ف ف

ف

ف

10

ق ق ق ق ق ق ق ق ق ق ق ق ق ق ق ق

ق

ق

ﻚ ﻚ ﻚ ﻚ ﻚ ﻚ ﻚ ﻚ ﻚ ﻚ ﻚ ﻚ ﻚ ﻚ ﻚ ﻚ ﻚ

ﻚ

ﻚ

و

و

و

ي

ي

ي

14

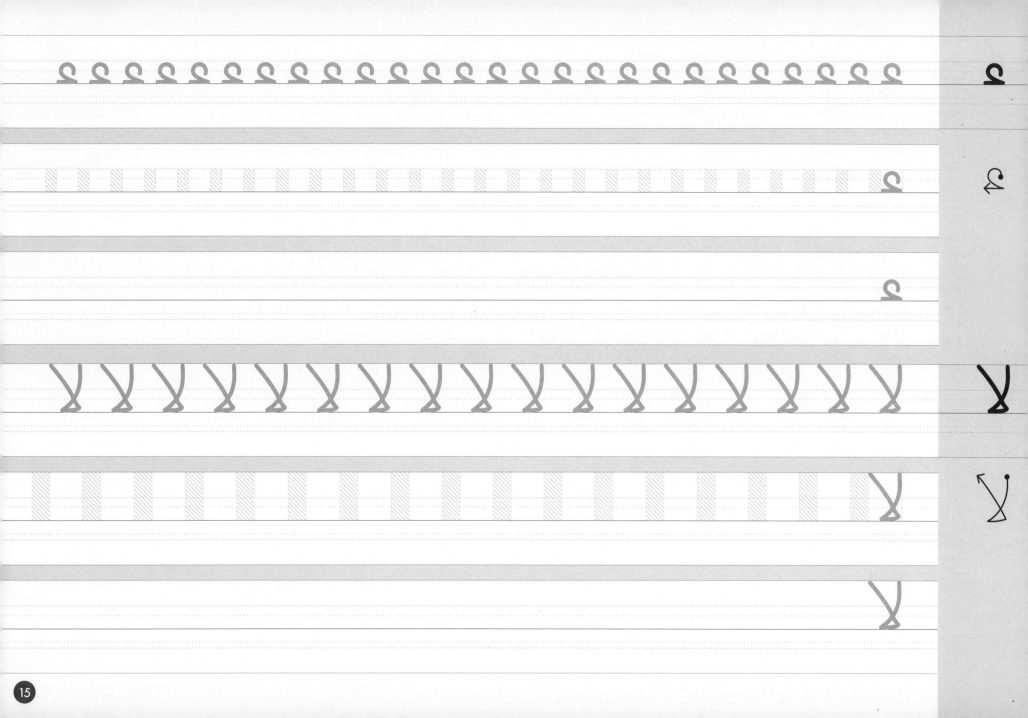

Write the alphabet out once more without the use of any guidelines. Compare your letter formations with the ones made at the beginning of the letters section. How much has your handwriting improved?

خ	ح	ج	ث	ت	ب	ا
ص	ش	س	ز	ر	ذ	د
ق	ف	غ	ع	ظ	ط	ض
ي	و	ه	ن	م	ل	ك

الحروف في الأول والوسط وآخر الكلمة

Letters at the Beginning, Middle and End of a Word

The letters of the Arabic alphabet change form when they appear at the beginning, middle or end of a word. The practice lines that follow have grouped letters together according to their shapes. For each letter, begin by tracing over the grey outline and then producing your own repetitions. Take special care to use the guidelines to ensure the correct height, width and positioning of each letter.

ا

ب ث ز ي   ﺮ

ﺑ ﯿ ﺜ ﺘ ﺑ   ﺑ

ﺑ ﺎ ﺗ ﺘ ﺚ   ﺳ

ن   ﻥ

ي   ﻱ

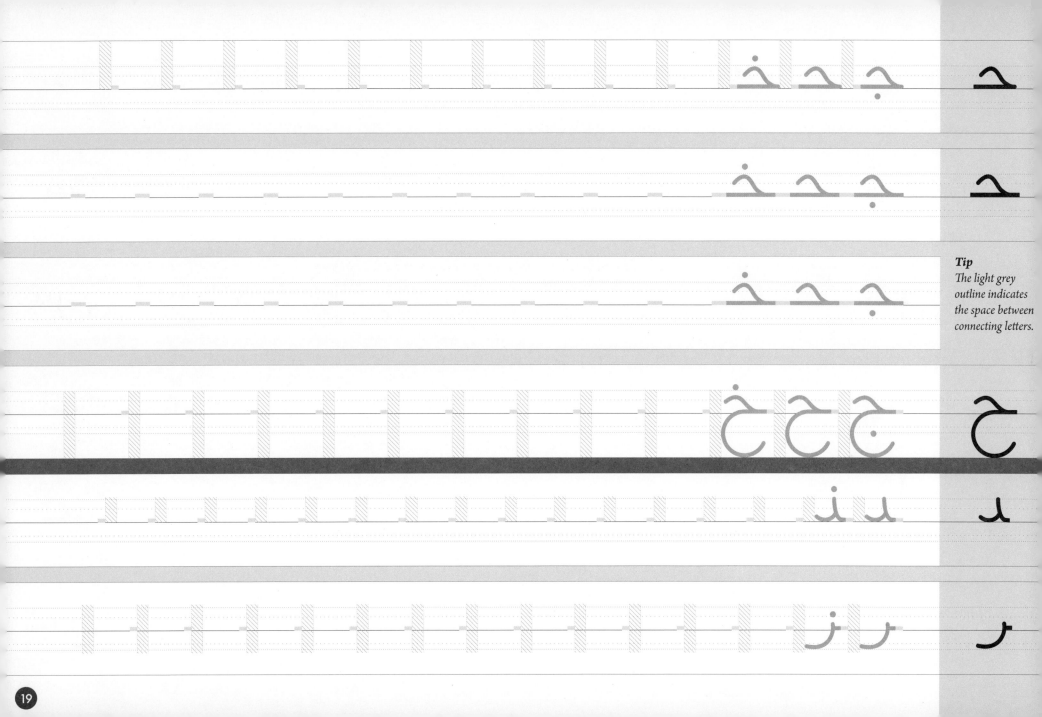

ـحـ ـجـ ـحـ ـخـ

ـحـ ـجـ ـحـ ـخـ

ـجـ ـحـ ـخـ

Tip
The light grey outline indicates the space between connecting letters.

ـح ـج ـح ـخ

ـد ـد ـذ

ـر ـر ـز

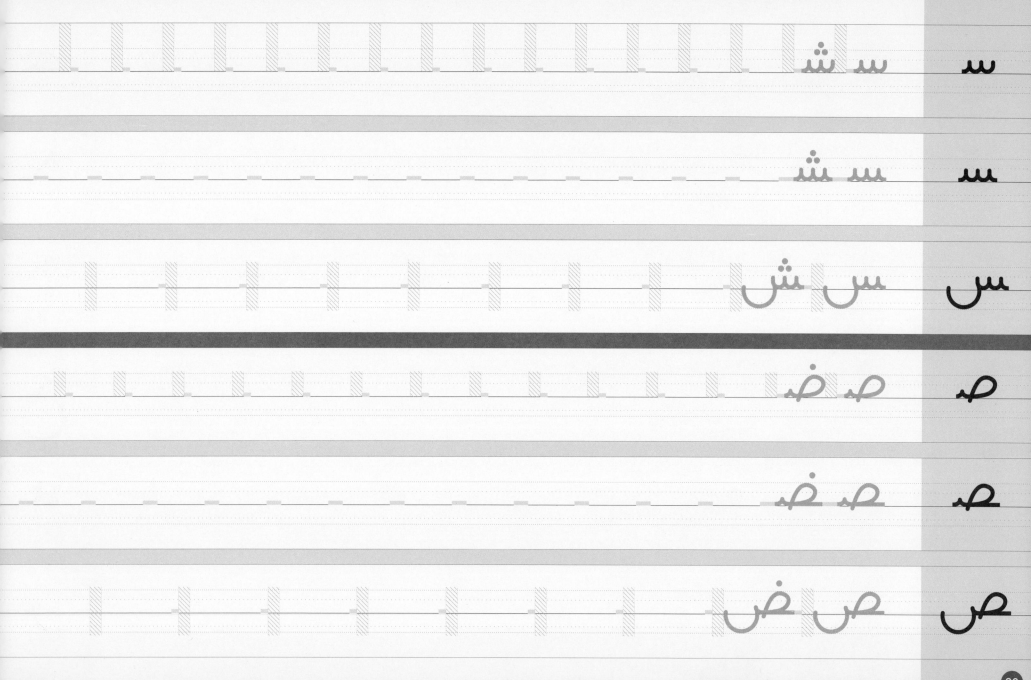

ظ ظ ظ

ظ ظ ظ

ظ ظ ظ

غ غ غ

ع ع ع

غ غ غ

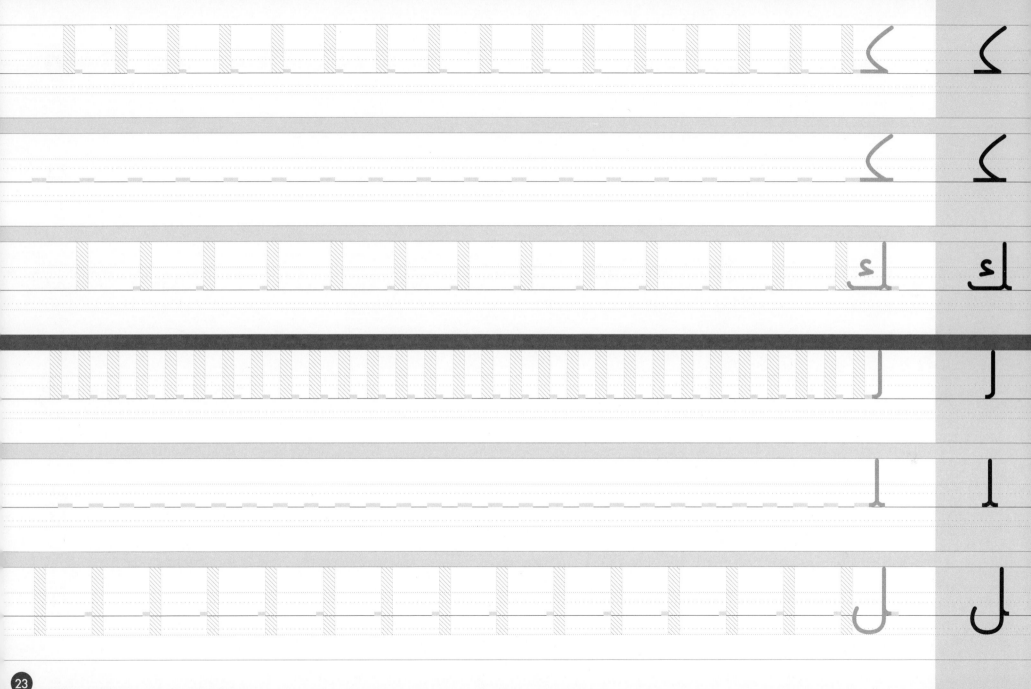

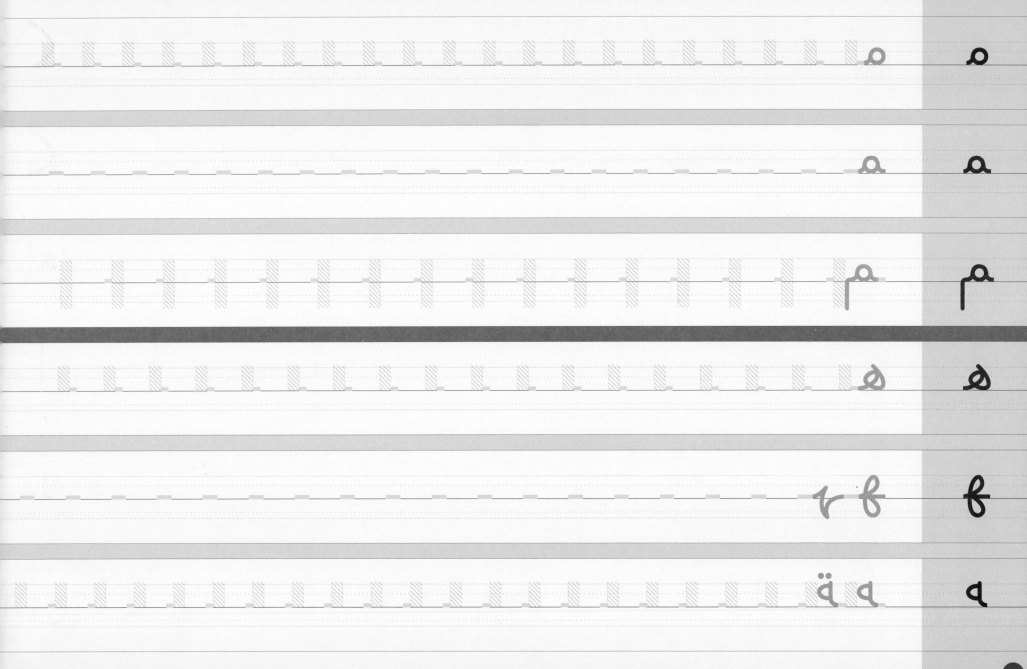

الكَلِمَات Words

Now that you are familiar with the letters of the alphabet and their variations at the beginning, middle and end of a word, you should be ready to begin composing words. Special care has been taken to ensure that the selection of words that follow contain every possible permutation of every letter, ensuring a comprehensive test of your skills. In this section, the size of the typeface gradually gets smaller as you progress. The word length also increases from two, three, four, five and six letter words, gradually preparing you for writing the sentences that follow in the next section.

SIZE REDUCED

truth	with him	with	to you*	he	how much	in	upon	what
حق	به	مع	لك	هو	كم	في	عن	ما
حق	به	مع	لك	هو	كم	في	عن	ما

26

to dispatch	touch	line	pilgrimage	bitter	hidden	shadow	script	hand
بث	مس	صف	حج	مر	سر	ظل	خط	يد
بث	مس	صف	حج	مر	سر	ظل	خط	يد

knowledge	heart	house	moon	night	sun
علم	قلب	بيت	قمر	ليل	شمس
علم	قلب	بيت	قمر	ليل	شمس

sea	mountain	garden	praise	Prophet	goodness
بحر	جبل	جنة	حمد	نبي	خير
بحر	جبل	جنة	حمد	نبي	خير

eye	to witness	king	virtue	patience	thankfulness
عين	شهد	ملك	فضل	صبر	شكر
عين	شهد	ملك	فضل	صبر	شكر

some	level	to destroy	to create	slave	to gather
بعض	طبق	هلك	خلق	عبد	جمع
بعض	طبق	هلك	خلق	عبد	جمع

as	with what	behind	to forget	cats	indeed
as	*with what*	*behind*	*to forget*	*cats*	*indeed*
كما	بما	خلف	نسي	قطط	لقد
كما	بما	خلف	نسي	قطط	لقد

as in the case	until	to silence	on	to prosper	stories
as in the case	*until*	*to silence*	*on*	*to prosper*	*stories*
نحو	حتى	سكت	على	فلح	قصص
نحو	حتى	سكت	على	فلح	قصص

parent (father)	progeny	children	tongue	way	tribulation
والد	ذرية	بنون	لسان	سبيل	فتنة

mosque	place	scholar	path	this world	belongings
مسجد	مكان	عالم	صراط	دنيا	متاع

reward	piety	wisdom	zakah	prayer	clear
ثواب	تقوى	حكمة	زكاة	صلاة	مبين

book	one	wing	spoken word	pure	good deed
كتاب	واحد	جناح	حديث	طيبة	حسنة

hour	group	the same	blessing	rewards	named
ساعة	فريق	سواء	نعمة	جزاء	مسمى

account	punishment	Messenger	close	great	sky
حساب	عذاب	رسول	قريب	عظيم	سماء

testimony	standing	ending	what an evil...	under her
شهادة	قيامة	عاقبة	بئسما	تحتها

on that day	those	good	group	between you
يومئذ	الذين	معروف	جماعة	بينكم

with us	glory	guidance	authority	upon them
عندنا	سبحان	هداية	سلطان	عليهم

The Forgiving	*The Merciful*	*The Thankful*	*The All Seeing*	*The All Hearing*
الغفور	الرحيم	الشكور	البصير	السميع

you have believed	*they know*	*to be victorious*	*they want*	*they say*
عامنتم	يعلمون	استنصر	يريدان	يقولون

The Woman Tested	*The Dispossessions*	*The Emissaries*	*The Wresters*	*The Defrauders*
الممتحنة	التغابن	المرسلات	النازعات	المطففين

34

Sentences الجُمَلُ

With word practice now complete, you should be ready to progress on to writing sentences. The selection of sentences presented in this section are drawn from Prophetic hadeeth and gradually increase in length, starting from two-word sentences. The handwriting size has been reduced once again and guidelines continue to be removed until only a single line remains at the end. This section ends with full paragraphs to complete your handwriting practice.

Indeed actions are by intentions. (Bukhari)

إنما الأعمال بالنيات

Purity is half of faith. (Muslim)

الطهور شطر الإيمان

Modesty is entirely good. (Bukhari)

الحياء خير كله

Every act of goodness is a charity. (Bukhari & Muslim)

كل معروف صدقة

The report is not like the witnessing. (Ahmed)

ليس الخبر كالمعاينة

Modesty is part of faith. (Muslim)

الحياء من الإيمان

Note
This is the first instance where a small hamza has been introduced on top of the letter alif.

36

Man (will be) with whom he loves. (Bukhari)

المرء مع من أُحب

Richness is the richness of the soul. (Bukhari)

الغنى غنى النفس

Do not hold back (in good) or (Allah) will withold from you. (Bukhari & Muslim)

لا توكى فيوكى عليك

He who cheats us is not from us. (Muslim)

ليس منا من غشنا

The one who guides to a good deed is like the doer of it. (Muslim)

الدال على الخير كفاعله

Meetings are under a trust. (Abu Dawood & Ahmed)

المجالس بالأمانة

He does not thank Allah who does not thank the people. (Abu Dawud & Ahmed)

لا يشكر الله من لا يشكر الناس

The wealth of a slave never decreased from giving in charity. (Tirmidhi)

ما نقص مال عبد من صدقة

Protect yourselves from Hellfire, even with part of a date. (Bukhari & Muslim)

اتقوا النار ولو بشق تمرة

This world is the believer's prison and the disbeliever's paradise. (Muslim)

الدنيا سجن المؤمن وجنة الكافر

Show mercy to those on earth and the One in the heaven will have mercy on you. (Tirmidhi)

ارحموا من في الأرض يرحمكم من في السماء

The repenter from sin is like one without sin. (Ibn Maajah)

التائب من الذنب كمن لا ذنب له

Note
Similar to the letter alif before, a small hamza has been introduced on top of the letter wow.

Note
A small hamza sits on top of a small nibrah, similar to the dots of the letters taa, thaa and noon.

عَنْ عُمَرَ رَضِيَ اللّٰهُ عَنْهُ أَيْضاً قَالَ بَيْنَمَا نَحْنُ جُلُوسٌ عِنْدَ رَسُولِ اللّٰهِ صَلَّى اللّٰهُ

عَلَيْهِ وَسَلَّمَ ذَاتَ يَوْمٍ إِذْ طَلَعَ عَلَيْنَا رَجُلٌ شَدِيدُ بَيَاضِ الثِّيَابِ شَدِيدُ سَوَادِ الشَّعْرِ

لَا يُرَى عَلَيْهِ أَثَرُ السَّفَرِ وَلَا يَعْرِفُهُ مِنَّا أَحَدٌ حَتَّى جَلَسَ إِلَى النَّبِيِّ صَلَّى اللّٰهُ

عَلَيْهِ وَسَلَّمَ فَأَسْنَدَ رُكْبَتَيْهِ إِلَى رُكْبَتَيْهِ وَوَضَعَ كَفَّيْهِ عَلَى فَخِذَيْهِ وَقَالَ يَا مُحَمَّدُ

أَخْبِرْنِي عَنِ الْإِسْلَامِ فَقَالَ رَسُولُ اللّٰهِ صَلَّى اللّٰهُ عَلَيْهِ وَسَلَّمَ الْإِسْلَامُ أَنْ تَشْهَدَ أَنْ

Note
This is the first instance where short vowels and other 'harakaat' have been added.

Tip
Although the sight of voweled words may appear daunting, the task is made easier if you add the 'harakaat' after having completed the writing of the words, sentences or paragraphs.

Also on the authority of 'Umar ﷺ, who said: "While we were one day sitting with the Messenger of Allah ﷺ, there appeared before us a man dressed in extremely white clothes and with very black hair. No traces of journeying were visible on him, and none of us knew him. He sat down close by the Prophet ﷺ, rested his knees against the Prophet's ﷺ knees and placed the palms of his hands on the thighs of the Prophet ﷺ, and said, "O Muhammad! Inform me about Islam." The Messenger of Allah ﷺ said, "Islam is that you should testify that …

لَا إِلَهَ إِلَّا اللَّهُ وَأَنَّ مُحَمَّدًا رَسُولُ اللَّهِ وَتُقِيمَ الصَّلَاةَ وَتُؤْتِيَ الزَّكَاةَ وَتَصُومَ رَمَضَانَ وَتَحُجَّ

الْبَيْتَ إِنِ اسْتَطَعْتَ إِلَيْهِ سَبِيلًا قَالَ صَدَقْتَ فَعَجِبْنَا لَهُ يَسْأَلُهُ وَيُصَدِّقُهُ قَالَ فَأَخْبِرْنِي

عَنِ الْإِيمَانِ قَالَ أَنْ تُؤْمِنَ بِاللَّهِ وَمَلَائِكَتِهِ وَكُتُبِهِ وَرُسُلِهِ وَالْيَوْمِ الْآخِرِ وَتُؤْمِنَ بِالْقَدَرِ

خَيْرِهِ وَشَرِّهِ قَالَ صَدَقْتَ قَالَ فَأَخْبِرْنِي عَنِ الْإِحْسَانِ قَالَ أَنْ تَعْبُدَ اللَّهَ كَأَنَّكَ تَرَاهُ فَإِنْ

لَمْ تَكُنْ تَرَاهُ فَإِنَّهُ يَرَاكَ قَالَ فَأَخْبِرْنِي عَنِ السَّاعَةِ قَالَ مَا الْمَسْؤُولُ عَنْهَا بِأَعْلَمَ مِنَ السَّائِلِ

Tip
Begin to explore your own personal style of handwriting. by making adjustments that you feel are necessary to suit your preferences.

Tip
When wrtiting quickly, try replacing two dots (..) with a short dash (▬), or a three dots (∴) with a small arrowhead (▲).

... there is no one worthy of worship but Allah and that Muhammad ﷺ is His Messenger and that you should establish the prayer, give the zakah, fast the month of Ramadan and perform Hajj to the House if you are able to do so." The man said, "You have spoken the truth." We were astonished at his questioning him and telling him that he was right. The man went on to say, "Inform me about iman." He, ﷺ answered, "It is that you believe in Allah and His Angels and His Books and His Messengers and in the Last Day, and in qadar, both in its good and in its evil aspects." He said, "You have spoken the truth." Then the man said, "Inform me about Ihsan." He, ﷺ answered, " It is that you should worship Allah as though you are seeing Him, and while you see Him not, yet truly He sees you." The man said, "Inform me about the Hour." He, ﷺ said, "The one questioned about it knows no more than the questioner." ...

قَالَ فَأَخْبِرْنِي عَنْ أَمَارَاتِهَا قَالَ أَنْ تَلِدَ الْأَمَةُ رَبَّتَهَا وَأَنْ تَرَى الْحُفَاةَ الْعُرَاةَ الْعَالَةَ رِعَاءَ

الشَّاءِ يَتَطَاوَلُونَ فِي الْبُنْيَانِ ثُمَّ انْطَلَقَ فَلَبِثْتُ مَلِيّاً ثُمَّ قَالَ يَاعُمَرُ أَتَدْرِي مَنِ السَّائِلُ

قُلْتُ اللّهُ وَرَسُولُهُ أَعْلَمُ قَالَ فَإِنَّهُ جِبْرِيلُ أَتَاكُمْ يُعَلِّمُكُمْ دِينَكُمْ

رَوَاهُ مُسْلِمٌ

عَنْ مُعَاذِ بْنِ جَبَلٍ رَضِيَ اللّهُ عَنْهُ قَلَ قُلْتُ يَارَسُولَ اللّهِ أَخْبِرْنِي بِعَمَلٍ يُدْخِلُنِي الْجَنَّةَ

… So the man said, "Well, inform me about its signs." So he, ﷺ said, "They are that the slave-girl will give birth to her mistress, that you will see the barefooted ones, the naked, the destitute, the herdsmen of the sheep competing with each other in raising lofty buildings." Thereupon the man went off. I waited a while, and then he ﷺ said, "O 'Umar, do you know who that questioner was?" I replied, "Allah and His Messenger know better." He, ﷺ said, "That was Jibril. He came to teach you your religion."" (Muslim)

From Mu'adh bin Jabal ﷺ, who said: I said: "O Messenger of Allah, tell me of a deed which will take me to Paradise …

وَيُبَاعِدُنِي عَنِ النَّارِ قَلَ لَقَدْ سَأَلْتَ عَنْ عَظِيمٍ وَإِنَّهُ لَيَسِيرٌ عَلَى مَنْ يَسَّرَهُ اللّٰهُ تَعَالَى

عَلَيْهِ تَعْبُدُ اللّٰهَ لَا تُشْرِكُ بِهِ شَيْئاً وَتُقِيمُ الصَّلَاةَ وَتُؤْتِي الزَّكَاةَ وَتَصُومُ رَمَضَانَ وَتَحُجُّ

الْبَيْتَ ثُمَّ قَلَ أَلَا أَدُلُّكَ عَلَى أَبْوَابِ الْخَيْرِ الصَّوْمُ جُنَّةٌ وَالصَّدَقَةُ تُطْفِئُ الْخَطِيئَةَ كَمَا

يُطْفِئُ الْمَاءُ النَّارَ وَصَلَاةُ الرَّجُلِ فِي جَوْفِ اللَّيْلِ ثُمَّ تَلَا ﴿تَتَجَافَى جُنُوبُهُمْ عَنِ

الْمَضَاجِعِ حَتَّى بَلَغَ ﴿يَعْمَلُونَ﴾ ثُمَّ قَالَ أَلَا أُخْبِرُكَ بِرَأْسِ الْأَمْرِ وَعَمُودِهِ وَذِرْوَةِ سَنَامِهِ

… and will keep me away from the Hell-fire." He said: "You have asked me about a great matter, yet it is, indeed, an easy matter for him to whom Allah Almighty makes it easy. (It is) that you worship Allah without associating anything with Him, that you perform the prayers, that you pay the zakat, that you fast during Ramadan, and that you make the pilgrimage to the House." Then he said: "Shall I not guide you to the gates of goodness? Fasting is a shield; charity extinguishes sin as water extinguishes fire; and a man's prayer in the middle of the night." Then he recited: "Who forsake their beds...for what they used to do". (As-Sajdah 32:16-17) Then he said: "Shall I not also tell you of the peak of the matter, its pillar, and its topmost part?" …

قُلْتُ بَلَى يَا رَسُولَ اللّهِ قَالَ رَأْسُ الْأَمْرِ الْإِسْلَامُ وَعَمُودُهُ الصَّلَاةُ وَذِرْوَةُ سَنَامِهِ الْجِهَادُ ثُمَّ

قَالَ أَلَا أُخْبِرُكَ بِمِلَاكِ ذَلِكَ كُلِّهِ قُلْتُ بَلَى يَارَسُولَ اللّهِ فَأَخَذَ بِلِسَانِهِ وَقَالَ كُفَّ عَلَيْكَ

هَذَا قُلْتُ يَانَبِيَّ اللّهِ وَإِنَّا لَمُؤَاخَذُونَ بِمَا نَتَكَلَّمُ بِهِ فَقَالَ ثَكِلَتْكَ أُمُّكَ يَامُعَاذُ وَهَلْ يَكُبُّ

النَّاسَ فِي النَّارِ عَلَى وُجُوهِهِمْ أَوْ قَالَ عَلَى مَنَاخِرِهِمْ إِلَّا حَصَائِدُ أَلْسِنَتِهِم

رَوَاهُ التِّرْمِذِيُّ وَقَالَ حَدِيثٌ حَسَنٌ صَحِيحٌ

… I said: "Yes, O Messenger of Allah." He said: "The peak of the matter is Islam, the pillar is prayer; and its topmost part is jihad." Then he said: "And shall I not tell you of the controlling of all that ?" I said:" Yes, O Messenger of Allah". So he took hold of his tongue and said: "Restrain this." I said: "O Prophet of Allah, will we be held accountable for what we say?" He said: "May your mother be bereft of you! Is there anything that topples people on their faces into the Hell-fire other than the jests of their tongues?" (Tirmidhi, who said it was a fine and sound hadith).